C000078711

jem
finally woken

Wise Publications
part of The Music Sales Group
London / New York / Paris / Sydney / Copenhagen / Berlin / Madrid / Tokyo

Published by
Wise Publications,
8/9 Frith Street, London, W1D 3JB, England.

Exclusive distributors:
Music Sales Limited,
Distribution Centre, Newmarket Road, Bury St Edmunds,
Suffolk, IP33 3YB, England.

Music Sales Pty Limited,
120 Rothschild Avenue, Rosebery,
NSW 2018, Australia.

Order No. AM92044
ISBN 0-7119-4174-2
This book © Copyright 2005 by Wise Publications,
a division of Music Sales Limited.

Music arrangements by Derek Jones.
Music processed by Paul Ewers Music Design.
Original design by JMJ@Skycycle.org
Front cover photograph by A. Cherry.
Back cover photograph by Paul Topp.
Page 3 & 4 photographs by Michael Lavine.

Printed in the United Kingdom.

www.musicsales.com

Your Guarantee of Quality:
As publishers, we strive to produce every book
to the highest commercial standards.

The music has been freshly engraved and the book has been
carefully designed to minimise awkward page turns and to make
playing from it a real pleasure. Particular care has been given
to specifying acid-free, neutral-sized paper made from pulps
which have not been elemental chlorine bleached.

This pulp is from farmed sustainable forests and
was produced with special regard for the environment.

Throughout, the printing and binding have been planned
to ensure a sturdy, attractive publication which should give
years of enjoyment.

If your copy fails to meet our high standards, please inform us
and we will gladly replace it.

they

Written by Jem Griffiths & Gerard Young
Incorporating elements from 'Prelude in F Minor'
by Ward Lamar Swingle and J.S.Bach

1. Who made up all the rules? We fol - low them like fools,
2. And it's i - ron - ic too, coz what we tend to do

come on closer

Written by Jem Griffiths & Gerard Young
Contains a sample of 'Baharon Phool Barsao'
written by Shankar Jaikishan/Hasrat Jaipuri

3. And now you're sa - tis - fied,   a twin - kle in your eye,   go to sleep for

ten.   And an - ti - ci - pa - ting,   I will be wait - ing

for you to wake a - gain.

Hot temp-ta-tions, sweet sen-sa-tions

in - fil - tra - ting through.

Sweet sen - sa - tions,

Play 3 times ad lib.

hot temp - ta - tions com - ing ov - er you.

Repeat to fade

finally woken

Written by Jem Griffiths
Bassline by Danny Griffin

16

save me

Written by Jem Griffiths & Gerard Young

save me, (ah,) wooh._____ Save me, (ah ah,)

save me, (ah ah,) save me, (ah,) wooh._____

2. Why would I think such things? Cra - zy thoughts have quick wings,
3. None of these thoughts are real so why is it that I feel

gain - ing mo - men - tum fast. Uh - huh, uh - huh.
so cut up and so bad?

save me, (ah ah,) save me, (ah,) wooh._____

Mir - ror mir - ror on the wall, who's the dumb - est of them all?

In - se - cu - ri - ties keep grow - ing, wast - ed en - er - gies are flow - ing.

An - ger, pain and sad - ness beck - on, pa - nic sets in, in a se - cond,

24

Written by Jem Griffiths & Justin Griffiths

1. Been gi - ven twen - ty four hours to tie___ up loose ends to make_ a - mends. His eyes___
2. Is there a hea - ven a hell and will___ I come back, who can tell? Now___

time._____ In twen-ty four hours_ they'll be lay-ing flow-ers on my

2° (eight - een)
3° (just eight)

life,_____ it's ov-er to - night._____ I'm not mess-ing, no I

need your bless-ing and your pro-mise to live free, please do it for me._____

Thir-teen hours_ they'll be lay-ing flow-ers on my life,_____ it's ov-er to-night.__

2° (Just one hour)_

28

missing you

Written by Jem Griffiths & Justin Griffiths

Don't think I ev - er be - lieved that___ this day would come._
All the won - der - ful mem - ories___ just make me fall a - part._

Now all I'm feel - ing is lost___ and numb.___ {And oh,___
And it feels like some - bo - dy's stabbed me___ in my heart.___

___ I know I pro - mised, mmmm,___ that I would try.___ But
2° that I wouldn't cry.___

I,___ yes I,___

31

wish i

Written by Jem Griffiths
Incorporating elements of 'Dearest'
by Ellas McDaniel's, Gibson & Polk

wish I_____ wish I was go-ing too.____

But if you

find that you___ don't___ like___ it, that the peo-ple there___ aren't in - vit -

just a ride

Written by Jem Griffiths & Mike Caren
Contains a sample from 'An Elephant Called Slowly' by Howard Blake

It's just a ride,__ it's just a ride,__ no need to run,__ no need to hide.__

__ It -'ll take__ you round and round,__ some-times you're up,__ some - times you're down.__

__ It's just a ride,__ it's just a ride,__ don't be scared, don't hide your eyes.__
*3° (now dry your eyes.)*__

Play 3 times

__ It may feel__ so real in - side,__ but don't for - get__ it's just a ride.
3° en - joy the ride.

It's just a ride,— it's just a ride,— no need to run,— no need to hide.—

Drums

It - 'll take— you all a - round,— some - times you're up,— some-times you're down.—

It's just a ride,— it's just a ride,— don't be scared,— now dry your eyes.—

It may feel— so real in - side,— but don't for - get— en - joy the ride.

falling for you

Written by Jem Griffiths, Brian Higgins & Nick Coler
Incorporating elements of "Moonlight Girl" by Moore

46

stay now

Written by Jem Griffiths, Klas Wahl, Marlene Moore,
Nicholas Whitecross, Klas Baggstrom & Lee Mason

Day-light comes,_ day-light comes_ and you've got-ta go.

Breaks my heart,__ breaks my heart__ to have to watch you go.

Wish I knew,__ wish I knew__ when you'll be

back a - gain. How - ev - er long,__ it's

just too long__ un - til we meet a - gain.

48

Stay now,__ stay now__ just a lit - tle more. Coz

this love,__ this love__ is what liv - ing's for.__

Stay now.__ Hide in bed,__ sheets

ov - er - head,__ block-ing out the sun.

Stay now,___ stay now___ just a lit-tle more.

Coz this love,___ this love___ is what

liv-ing's for.___ Stay now.___

Stay now.___

flying high

Written by Jem Griffiths & Paul Herman

1. You can't know,_ oh no, you can't know_ how much I_____ think a-bout_
2. I know,_ oh yes, I know_ that we can't_____ be to-geth-

123456789